1838

GREAT WE...

The "Great Western" of the Great Western Steam ship company took 15 days 5 hours from Liverpool to New York at an average speed of 8.8 knots.

RIBAND

1907

The "Mauretania" of the Cunard Line took 4 days 22 hours 53 minutes from Sandy Hook to Daunt's Rock at an average speed of 23.69 knots.

MAURETANIA

£4.99

HOTSPUR
BOOK FOR BOYS
1988

CONTENTS

STORIES

	Page
The Goalie from Golunga	5
X-Bow versus the Animals	17
The Sword and the Staff	28
The Swamp Rat	33
Starhawk	42
The Big Palooka	49
Mantracker	58
Spring-Heeled Jack	65
Medic Muldoon	74
Sergeant Sixty	81
The Thing from the Pit	89
Rocky Rhodes	97
Larry had to Learn	108
Coonskin Grenadier	113
Underwater Wonders	120

FEATURES

	Page
The Blue Riband	2 and 126
The Mitsubishi Zero	15
The Douglas Dakota	26
Lord of the Plains	41 and 112
The Me 262	65
The Short Sunderland	72
The Me 165 Komet	87
The Flying Fortress	106

Printed and Published in Great Britain by D. C. THOMSON & CO., LTD.,
185 Fleet Street, London EC4A 2HS.
© D. C. THOMSON & CO., LTD., 1987.
ISBN 0-085116-394-7

The GOALIE from GOLUNGA

Keep Wally under pressure! We're not just here for fun!

FEW people know how First Division Emstock United came to sign their star goalie, Ben Colby. After drawing 0-0 with Sanfisisco in the first leg of the European Cup semi-final, Manager Bert Fenton took his players, including England goalie, Wally Page, to the small African state of Golunga to tune up for the return game.

...followed by another...

...but—

You missed it, Page!

As the United players followed their manager's instructions, Wally Page made a fine save...

Who's the smart guy?

Huh! Missed again!

6

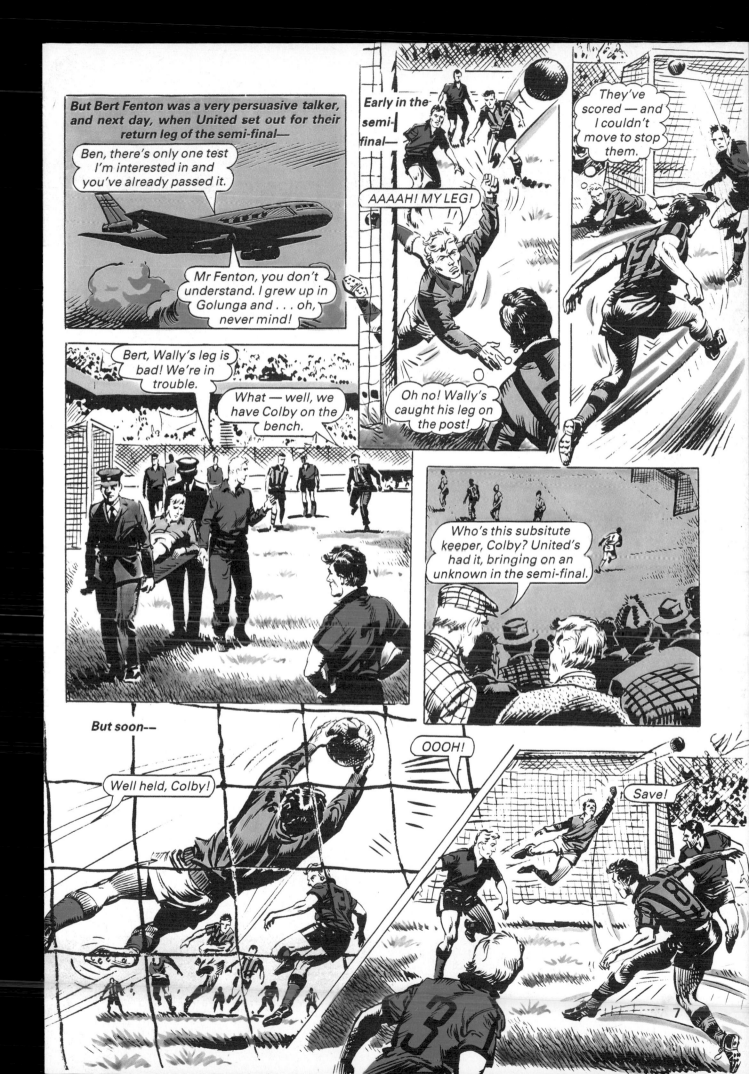

Gaining confidence in Ben, United pressed forward.

To me, Jimmy! To me!

Goal! Come on United! We need another one!

The minutes ticked away, then—

To me! Pass it back!

Not much time to go! I'll try to put Tony clear.

To you, Tony!

Goal! Colby's clearance made that one!

United were through to the final.

You played a blinder, youngster! You'll be in the team for the final!

Well . . . er . . . I'm not sure . . . there's . . .

8

Ben played the remaining League games. Then three days before the final . . .

What news of Wally, Bert?

His leg's still playing up. There's no way he'll be fit for the final. A good job we have young Colby!

But we haven't. Colby left for Golunga this morning. Something about special tests.

He can't do that!

Two hours later—

I'm going after Colby. Unless I can bring him back for the final we've had it — not a hope!

Bert reached Golunga.

You stay with us! You no see Colby!

But I have to see him.

Fenton was escorted to the edge of the village.

Today Colby proves he is worthy as Keeper of the Sacred Scroll of Komanso. He is our chosen. He must take the tests!

Tests! What are they talking about?

That's Colby climbing the tree. NO!

Silence!

9

A lion enclosure! Surely he isn't —

Are you ready?

I am ready. Open the door!

Ben slid lithely into the enclosure.

No! Colby has to collect that football tied to the meat.

GRRAAAAAA!

Timing is vital. There will be no second chance—

Got it! Now to get out of here!

111

Ben dived desperately—

Close the gate!

Hurrah!

Colby, you are indeed worthy to be chosen Keeper of the Scroll. But now you have another test, beyond the seas.

The other test was the European Cup final against Valenia. Ben was soon in action.

Saved, Colby!

Hurrah!

Down the left, Gary — quickly!

Your's, Bill! Travel with it!

12

THE MITSUBISHI ZERO

THE Japanese entered the Second World War on December 7, 1941, with a treacherous raid on the big American naval base at Pearl Harbour, Hawaii. In the forefront of the attack was Japan's most fearsome war-weapon, the Zero fighter!

The first journey of the prototype Zero back in March 1939 was neither fast nor elegant. The factory where it was built had no runway, and the machine had to be carried to the nearest military airfield on an ox-cart!

The new fighter saw its first combat in August, 1940, while Japan was fighting against China. They escorted bombers over the Chinese cities and performed aerobatics over airfields, trying to get their adversaries to come up and fight!

When at last the two sides met in a fight, 13 Japanese fighters pounced on 27 Russian-built I-15 and I-16 fighters and shot down every one.

Soon after Pearl Harbour, the Japanese struck at America's big air base in the Philippines. Again, the Americans were taken by surprise. Unescorted bombers they could have dealt with, but the amazing Zero fighters had flown all the way from Formosa! The range of the Zero for this mission was an incredible 1200 miles!

15

Sadly underestimated by Britain and America, the Zero fighter was already proving a big surprise!

Zero A6M5.

Engine—Nakijima Sakae 21.
Top Speed—351 m.p.h. Rate of climb—4500 ft. per min.
Ceiling—36000 feet. Span 36ft. 1in. Length 29ft. 9in.

The R.A.F. flew Brewster Buffalos over Malaya. These were no match for the Zeros!

GRUMMAN WILDCAT

Not until later models of the manoeuvrable Spitfire arrived on the scene did the R.A.F. have any success. The other old American fighters were also outclassed.

The only fighters to have much success against the Zero at first were the American Volunteer Group—the famous "Flying Tigers", commanded by Major-General Claire Chennault. Their tactics were to dive their heavy P-40 Tomahawks into a formation of the more nimble Zeros, rely on surprise marksmanship, then pull out and run for safety at top speed!

But outside the Flying Tigers operating area, the Zeros flew triumphantly on. Japan's entire war hopes rested firmly on them. Pilots like Nishizawa, with a score of 102 kills continued to sweep opposition aside in the conquest of the Pacific.

CURTISS MOHAWK

The Battle of Midway was a turning-point for the Zero, as Japan's most potent war-weapon. While they fought American torpedo-bombers at low level, dive-bombers attacked by surprise and sank their three aircraft carriers. It was a vital blow.

ZEROS BELOW. LET'S GET 'EM BEFORE THEY SPOT US! DIVE!

After that, the day of the Zero was nearly over. A new breed of American fighter began to come into action. From mid-1943, few Zeros could return from combat without damage.

LOCKHEED LIGHTNING

GRUMMAN HELLCAT

VOUGHT CORSAIR

Attempts to modify the Zero were too late and largely unsuccessful. In desperation, the Japanese turned to Kamikaze raids. The first suicide planes were bomb-carrying Zeros.

The final version of the Zero took the sky in April, 1945. The Zero 64 was faster, more powerful, better armed and protected yet just as agile as before—but it was too late. American bombers were by that time hitting hard at Japan itself, and the war was lost.
In its day, the Zero was the world's best carrier-based fighter, and master of the Pacific skies.

16

X-BOW VERSUS The ANIMALS

It's just a harmless, tranquilliser gas. No charge, Rhino!

Now for the animals I'm not going to treat gently!

They're not keen on me either! Grenades! Not a bit friendly!

I'll fix one with a "bug" for direction-finding. So we'll meet again!

71-3

Klik!

Since the bug's signal had only a short range, it took time before X-Bow could detect it again—

Hullo, there's the bleeper! I'm in luck and in business.

There's the bike. All I need to do is wait until its owner shows up. Ah, the balcony will do fine.

They descended together—

What X-Bow had learned meant he had to act swiftly—

I'm glad you saw sense. I'll take you somewhere safe till I've dealt with your buddies.

You-you . . . I'll get you for this!

The Animals mean to hit the great funland centre tonight. It'll be closed but they'll rob it and wreck it.

As long as I'm here first, I'm happy. I'll wait.

Never waste jump jet power when there's a ramp handy!

I always fancied a free ride on a Switchback. And it makes a good lookout too!

TICKETS

21

GHOST MILL

It's a dead end! We're trapped!

Use the mill! Dump the bike and run for it!

This way! I've switched on the power.

EXIT

GHOST

EEEEEEEEOOOOOOOOOOO!

Well, it's different but they can't go far!

They've quite gone to pieces. Shooting at everything — even the ghosts!

That's enough, you guys! You hit the wrong ghost and he turned nasty!

The funland folk will be pleased to find you. They might even keep you, you look so horrible!

The alarm had been given—

The Animals have all been captured. I hope they'll like it behind bars!

With the protection racket broken, many people were more than just grateful. By secret means, X-Bow was paid—

Someone left this for you, Bud. Wouldn't give a name. Just said, 'Thanks!'

And so—

It's your lucky day, kids! A free run of the fair. Let's start with the Switchback and Ghost Mill!

ENTRANC

Gee, you must be rich, Mister.

Not really! I just like to spread enjoyment around.

The End

THE DOUGLAS
DAKOTA

DURING the Second World War, no aircraft served with more distinction than the Douglas D.C.3. It flew through shot and shell, delivering its vital war-loads, without a single gun to fight back with.

The Douglas D.C.3 was designed in response to an urgent request by American airline chiefs. It went into service in 1936. Known as the Douglas Sleeper Transport, it brought the airlines back from the brink of financial disaster.

GEE, MOM, CAN WE REALLY SLEEP IN THIS AIRPLANE?

Soon every American airline and many European ones were flying D.C.3's. Deliveries were made at the rate of six per month, and by 1939, 90 per cent of the world's airline business was being flown on 21-seater D.C.3's.

The aircraft built up a tremendous reputation for reliability. It was very easy to fly and there were amazingly few crashes.

First World War ace pilot Eddie Rickenbacker just escaped death in a rare D.C.3 disaster.

In 1941, the D.C.3 went to war! Many airline planes were pressed into Air Force service. The R.A.F. bought some surplus planes for use in the Middle East. They christened the aircraft "Dakota."

Technical details—

Wingspan - 95 ft.
Speed - 206 m.p.h. cruising, 235 m.p.h. maximum.

Length - 64 ft. 5 in.
Height - 14 ft. 11 in.

Passengers - 21-28 max.
Payload 5000 lb. at 340-mile range.

The Dakota became the workhorse of the Allied air forces. It carried millions of tons of war equipment —and dropped 4381 paratroops on to the German - held island of Sicily, in 1943.

Every task the Dakota was asked to do, it did without complaint. They even put floats on it and used it as a seaplane! It was the standard troop-transport and glider tug.

They even tried it as a glider itself. Only the fact that the engine nacelles were retained on the wings hampered it from keeping in the air better than any real glider designed for the job!

LOOK AT THAT GOONEY BIRD GO!

IS THERE ANYTHING THESE CRATES CAN'T DO?

Only designed to carry 21 passengers, the Dakota often took more—many more—as during the evacuation of Burma!

I SAY, THAT'S 74 MEN CRAMMED IN THERE! THAT AEROPLANE WILL NEVER LEAVE THE GROUND!

DON'T YOU BELIEVE IT! ALL SHE'LL NEED ARE A FEW EXTRA INCHES AND SHE'LL LIFT THE LOT.

The pilot was right. That Dakota established a weight-lifting record!

The Dakota has the distinction of being the only transport plane to be officially credited with shooting down an enemy fighter! Over the Pacific—

LOOK OUT—THAT ZERO'S GONNA HIT US!

WOULDYA BELIEVE IT—MOST OF THE RUDDER'S GONE BUT THE OLD GIRL'S STILL UNDER CONTROL. WE'RE GONNA GET HOME LIKE THIS!

THAT ZERO AIN'T, THOUGH! WE'VE GOT US A FIGHTER!

One of the most incredible sights of the Second World War was a string of Douglas D.C.3 Dakotas, four abreast and almost 200 miles long, spearheading the airborne invasion of Normandy!

In many parts of the world, the faithful Dakota still flies on, though no longer in airline or military service. Perhaps the longest and slowest journey ever undertaken by a Dakota is that started by one which crashed into the snowfield of a Swiss glacier. Experts reckon it won't come out into the bottom of the valley for 600 years!

We have no need to explain ourselves to strangers! Die, foreigners!

Looks like we'll have to try a little persuasion, Amos. It'd be a shame to have to resort to violent means . . .

Within minutes—

It would seem they've had enough, gentlemen. My thanks and admiration for your support. Without it, I'd not have lived long.

Odds life, Amos! I'd forgotten all about the poor chap!

Later, over a snack by a stream . . .

Were those hill-bandits after your money, friend?

No. They'll soon have more than enough of that. The French are sending many thousands of pounds in gold to bribe the hill tribes to rise up against the King!

That will force King Edward to divide his forces. He'll weaken his numbers engaged against those French!

A devilish plan. So that's why they were trying to silence you, friend!

But, alas, there is little I can do now. I'll never reach the King with the news in time. The French boat lands here tomorrow night . . .

Then we must do what we can on our own, brother. Show us the spot where these Frenchmen will come ashore with the gold . . .

Later—

Well, we can't harm them at sea, Richard, and we can't attack them as they land because their backs will be to the sea and they could simply cast-off again . . .

That means we must tackle them up here with whatever natural help we can bring to bear . . .

29

And so, the following night . . .

Here they come! Let's get ready!

Now!

The armed guide fell first . . .

Arrgh!

Number one! Now for the men behind the mules!

Arrgh!

Urgh!

Mon Dieu! Take cover! We are sitting targets up here!

Now, Amos! NOW!

Then—

Off you go, you hairy brutes! GO! GO! Go drive these foreigners from your hills!

Look out! Mountain goats! They'll drive us from the ledge! Go back—go back!

Must get the mules—aargh!

It worked beautifully! They've been driven back! And the mules are ours for the taking!

All done nice and simply, brothers. Once we have the mules, we can keep those French at bay with simple rear-guard tactics!

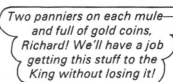

Two panniers on each mule—and full of gold coins, Richard! We'll have a job getting this stuff to the King without losing it!

True, Amos, but there's something about these—

Then—

So! The thieves would seem to have fallen into an ambush themselves! Shall we kill them now—or have sport with them later, men?

Hold hard, hill-man! Lower your weapons or I scatter this gold down every crack and crevice on this hillside. It would take you months or even years to recover it all!

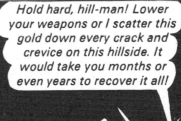

Hold! He is right. If he slays the mules, they'll fall and we'll lose the gold.

Let us live and you can have the French gold. Is that a fair enough bargain, hill-men?

Aye! Though I'd not value your puny lives so highly!

WHAT! You can't be serious, Richard! You can't bargain with a brigand!

At the top of the track . . .

One move from above and I despatch the mules!

Go your ways in peace! Just give us the French gold.

I never thought I'd live to see the day Richard Brand backed away from a fight—and bargained for his life with gold!

We should have died rather than part with that French gold, Richard. Now nothing can stop the uprisings!

You're too pessimistic, Amos—not to say lacking trust in your old friend. Just follow me and keep a close watch.

Leaping onto his horse, Richard led them back along the ridge. Then—

We'll see some fun soon, brothers. The Welsh hill-bandits are counting their gold—and the French soldiers are on their way!

What is there to be so high-spirited about, Richard. We have failed in our task!

As the trio watched, a roar went up from the bandit chief.

WHAAAA—! Those French dogs!

What's happening? Did you know about this, Richard?

Aye, Amos! It's just as I suspected. This is where the fun begins.

You scum! Die! Destroy the dogs!

Arrrgh! Aieeee!

I—I don't understand! What's going on? Those bandits are slaughtering the French!

And it serves them right, Amos! The French were using a kind of Pinchbeck— a false gold. They hoped to deliver it and be away before the hillmen realised it was false. Once the troubles had started, it wouldn't matter.

False gold! Those Frenchmen were idiots if they thought they could fool the bandits with that stuff. If there's one thing those hillmen know — it's gold!

The End

The SWAMP RAT

THERE are many stories to the legend of the Swamp Rat, set in time before the Second World War — stories of a white boy taken by Dyak pirates from a raided ship and raised by them in the river-slashed wilderness of South-West Borneo. One story begins with a happening by night in the Makasar Strait . . .

Day came . . .

Lookum, Captain Twiss!

A sea monster . . .

Out cold, but the only damage seems to be this bump on the head. Not much more we can do for him right now.

He's just a youngster and white! Yet the tattooing on him looks Dyak.

Same like knife. This Dyak killing barong.

The pearling lugger 'BANDA STAR' went about her business . . .

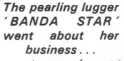

Here's the spot where the best beds are. Heave-to and the boys can go down.

33

The BANDA STAR made sail . . .

Good! They've been frightened away!

Round the other side is a bay where we can pitch a shore camp. Tomorrow, we'll try again.

Son, there's a tale going round the South Seas of a white boy who was raised by Dyaks and saved the lives of a survey team lost in the jungle. He was called the Swamp Rat and I heard he'd been sent to school in Australia.

That's me, Captain. I decided to graduate myself back to the long huts of my Dyak kinfolk.

Next day . . .

Captain Twiss, them fellah divers not go down in this bad place. Them ask we go lookum for other shell beds.

Captain, the only way find out exactly what the shark position is, is for somebody to go in.

Ain't nothing to worry about boys, a muster of sharks like yesterday ain't likely to happen again for months!

The Swamp Rat went in . . . deep . . .

There's that noise again. Like bats squeaking in my head!

It gets louder in this direction. I'll follow it.

The Swamp Rat came free...

You'd better come in as well, Mister Japanese!

We can throw some grenades in and the concussion will force him up.

No need! Ach—look!

Sharks come to the call of my apparatus.

The intruder is taken by a shark!

Fool! That was my crewman!

I'd better leave before things get too hot.

The sharks don't seem interested now their call to dinner's been put out of action!

The top blew off the Isle of the Dead...

Boys, this is one of those days when it's no use trying to get any work done! Everything's against us!

LOOKUM, CAPTAIN TWISS!

BANDA STAR

The Swamp Rat was hauled again aboard the BANDA STAR...

Son, what you say means those Japs are building up for a war. Maybe you'd be better off back at school in Australia.

I'll carry on where I'm going, Captain. Me and the Dyaks will be ready if any warring Japs come our way!

THE END

LORDS OF THE PLAINS — THE STORY OF THE BUFFALO

CENTURIES ago, when the great glaciers still covered the Earth, the ancestors of the buffalo first arrived in North America, over the Bering Strait, which was then iced over to form a link with Asia.

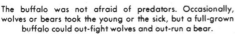

Really a bison, the American buffalo was a massive, fierce-looking creature, sometimes reaching a ton in weight. Buffalo tended to roam in huge numbers and once, in 1871, a herd was seen which was claimed to be "about 12 million"!

The buffalo was not afraid of predators. Occasionally, wolves or bears took the young or the sick, but a full-grown buffalo could out-fight wolves and out-run a bear.

Only natural causes like quicksands, thin ice on river-crossings or extra severe winters kept the numbers of the buffalo under control.

The Indians of the plains depended on the buffalo for food, clothing and other necessities of life. Long before the white man introduced the horse to America, they hunted the buffalo by driving them over cliffs.

Their tepees were made from buffalo hides stretched over thin poles. Buffalo robes were worn, and buffalo meat was eaten. The meat could be preserved by drying out, cutting into strips then pouring on molten fat to make 'pemmican'.

When the white man introduced the horse to America, the Plains Indians soon learned a more effective—if no less dangerous—way to hunt their buffalo.

But the thousands of railroad workers had to be fed, and buffalo meat proved to be ideal. Then began the biggest-ever threat to the Lords of the Plains!

In the 1850's, the railroads began to spread throughout the West. The buffalo were a source of great annoyance to the railway surveyors, using their carefully erected markers for scratching posts!

Turn to PAGE 112 for PART TWO of the story of the buffalo!

CENTURY 26AD... the galaxy-spanning Terran Empire is crumbling in decline. With the alien Krell ravaging its margins, its order is replaced by chaos and the dawn of a new barbarism amid which one man stands for law and as helper of the oppressed... Sol Rynn, known as...

STARHAWK

At a small primitive farming settlement on the planet Procyon-Four.

Don't kill them all! We need some to work for us!

Run! Run for your lives!

The card! I must use the card Trader Jakus left!

I'll fit this into the communicator, and . . .

Stop, boy!

You will send no messages!

AARHHH!

But the message had been transmitted in time!

Distress call coming through. It emanates from Procyon-Four!

Procyon-Four? Never heard of it! Well, we'll head for it now!

On board were Starhawk and his robot companion, Droid—

Procyon-Four — Earth-type planet lacking in minerals, suited to small settlement and subsistance farming. In neutral zone, so no weapons allowed.

Must be one of those backwaters where Trader Jakus handed out my cards.

And so—

The communicator would be in the main village — or what was the main village, Mister Rynn.

Such crude weapons mean it isn't Krell work. More like local feuding among the settlers.

Mister Rynn, my sensory units detect a living organism close by. Near the communicator!

Savage men from the mountain attacked us with clubs and spears . . . killing, burning. I saw some of my people driven away as prisoners. I was left for dead!

Leaving Droid to take the boy for medical attention, Starhawk went scouting on a ground-sled—

Droid, I'm on a trail-line. Odd patches of soft ground show human footprints.

Mister Rynn, radiation registers in the direction you are headed. I would suggest uranium deposits were it not that this planet is lacking in minerals.

Droid, I am beaming you through on the sled's video-scan. Something of interest has just appeared ahead . . .

. . . a valley — with some kind of manual activity.

Those baldies must be the savage men. They appear to have their prisoners building some type of fortification.

So the sled-scan shows me, Mister Rynn. It also shows that you would be wise to make a quick shift of position.

WHAT THE . . .?

KLUNK!

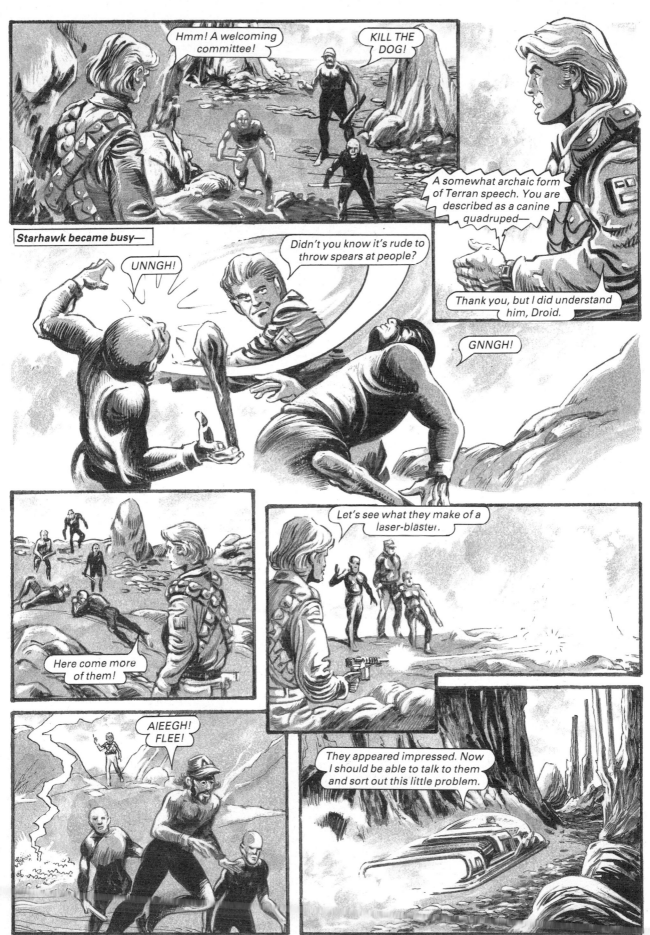

Starhawk was met by a reception committee—

Come closer and the slaves die. Even your great weapon cannot save them.

That is a smart rascal, Droid. He uses human wickedness against human softness.

All I can do is turn away!

Mister Rynn, you are now heading towards that radiation of which I spoke.

Droid! A ship!

A spacecraft of extremely early design, Mister Rynn — thrust-driven by a crude form of fission motor.

You mean it's not a warper, but a sub-light traveller. Great Nova, it must have taken centuries to get here.

Hundreds of what look like sleeping compartments, Droid.

More likely freezer units, Mister Rynn. Early ships carried crews and passengers in deep freeze to combat the long travel time of even short hauls in space.

Here's one who didn't thaw out too well.

Mister Rynn, the savage men are gathering outside the vessel.

Obviously they've talked it over and decided to make peace with the owner of such a mighty weapon.

But when Starhawk walked out—

Now! Snare the dog.

WHAT THE . . .?

To the rocks with him.

Mister Rynn, this is an odd prelude to talking peace!

Droid, stop dawdling, and do something!

Relief action has been initiated, Mister Rynn.

LOOK!

Centuries ago, Earth decided to exile its dangerous criminals. They were despatched on a fission-powered ship, programmed to commence revival after landfall at a suitable Earth-type planet.

Phew! You mean that hulk's been plodding through the galaxy for five hundred years carrying a load of frozen baldies?

I have you in the traction-beam, Mister Rynn!

What magic is this?

Droid, we need a safe way to lay out that bunch of antique villains.

I suggest a harmless, yet disabling, nerve gas, Mister Rynn!

Starhawk made a gassing run—

It means knocking out both locals and baldies, but we'll sort out the sheep from the goats when both lots are snoozing, Droid.

Some of your speech terms still puzzle me, Mister Rynn.

We'll put those bald lads back into deep freeze, then we'd better tow that hulk somewhere where they can't do any harm.

No need of any towing, Mister Rynn. I can easily refuel and energise the vessel's reaction pile. They should all be unconscious by now!

Soon have them all on board. Then we can shoot them into space and revive the others!

Starhawk, where do you send those evil men?

Back where they came from, my friend — a return of unwanted rubbish.

Starhawk departed—

A thousand years to end up where they set off from. They'll be able to claim a record round trip — if anybody is still on Earth when they get there!

THE END

THE BIG PALOOKA

NEW YORK, on a summer's day in 1956. Sergeant Joe Rooney of the New York Police awaited the arrival of Sergeant Jim Ransom from Scotland Yard. A temporary exchange of sergeants had been arranged between the two forces and Captain Mike Logan had given Rooney the job of looking after the British sergeant . . .

Oh, no, not that! Don't tell me I'm gonna be stuck with that!

The Big Palooka! Fancy being nursemaid to a big, dopey Limey!

Hullo, there's Fingers Phillips and Knocker Morris heading for the Big Palooka. They picked him out as an easy mark. Knocker will bang into him and Fingers will steal his wallet. Better stop 'em I reckon —

Wait a minuto! The Limey cop no sooner sets foot on American soil than a smart pickpocket steals his money, I'll let Fingers carry on, then I'll grab him!

But things did not quite work out as Rooney or the pickpockets expected!

OUCH!

I suppose you think the little guy had his mitt in the other guy's pocket to keep it warm? He's Fingers Phillips, our top pickpocket, and that hunk o' meat there is his hustler, Knocker Morris.

Say, that Big Palooka ain't such a Palooka as he looks!

I'd like to see you talk your way out of this one, Fingers. Talk about being caught red-handed? Okay, Doyle. Take these guys to your precinct house and book them.

Yarooh! Hey, Mr Rooney, tell him to let go. I'll come quietly. He's bustin' my hand!

Sure thing, Sergeant. What's the charge?

I'm Joe Rooney of Logan's Detective Squad. You'll be Jim Ransom of the British C.I.D. Mighty smart bit o' work you did there, Jim.

Glad to know you, Rooney. I've had some experience of pickpockets and knew what to expect. Sorry I had to give that poor chap a tap on the jaw.

Wow, you've got a grip like a bear. No wonder that tap o' yours made Knocker come over all queer! Come on, I'll take you to meet Captain Logan and Lieutenant Miagli.

Rooney quickly drove Ransom to Central Street police station, where Captain Mike Logan and Lieutenant Lou Miagli were waiting —

D

Pleased to meet you, Ransom — and I hope this will be the first of many exchanges between officers and men of New York and London.

Thank you, sir. We also have high hopes of this scheme.

You'll get plenty of action here, Ransom. This is the general purpose squad. We handle anything so you'll get plenty of experience of all types of crime. Have you a gun?

No, sir. The Police in Britain don't carry guns.

Get that "sir" line! The Limey is trying to butter up Logan.

Well, the crooks over here carry guns so I'll not be responsible for you until you get a gun.

That "sir" business ain't soft-soaping, Lou. They just have stronger discipline in England.

HUH!

If you insist, sir. I can't buy an expensive gun, but I'll buy the best I can.

Fair enough, Ransom.

You'll start work tomorrow. Joe Rooney will show you the ropes.

Very good, sir — and thank you!

Rooney took Ransom to a trustworthy gunsmith's, leaving him to buy his own gun —

Next morning, at the target practice in the basement —

Well, if it ain't the Limey. I suppose you've been able to buy a gun you can afford?

Yes, but it wasn't easy. I had to take practically the cheapest in the shop.

Well come on, then. Let's have a look at it!

Ransom produced a long, old-fashioned Colt .45 —

Where did you get that old thumb-buster?

I decided to buy an old second-hand gun in good condition in preference to a cheap new one which was liable to burst its barrel after a few shots.

Sergeant Carter, holder of the coveted Delbond Medal for Marksmanship and the best shot of the force, examined the gun —

It's old, but it's in good shape. It won't let you down — say, Ransom, ain't I seen you some place before?

50

The first shot was Ransom's sighting shot and, after he had discovered that the gun pulled to the right, he corrected his aim and put five shots into the target with machine-gun-like rapidity —

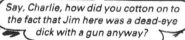

51

As the police car roared across town to the National Bank, Sergeant Rooney told Ransom about the gangsters. Weist's mob were the toughest gang of bank robbers in the country. Ruthless killers, they had sworn they would never be taken alive.

We're too late! Get under cover.

You ain't stoppin' us, Cops!

Johnny! Give us covering fire with the machine-gun. Three of us go to the right and the others will go left. We'll outflank them. Let's go!

Gurney has hit Johnny! Ransom, Rooney, Josephs go after Gurney. He's got us pinned down.

Hey, Ransom — you're going the wrong way!

Well what do you think of your crack marksman now? He's getting outa here as fast as he can!

And I suppose the fact that you were also getting yourelf out of a gun battle didn't enter into your calculations at all!

I got back into the fight as soon as possible. In fact, I think you will find that one of the bandits has a bullet from my gun in his leg.

Well, we'll never know till we catch up with them, will we?

Hm. I wonder if it would work?

Looks like Weist is heading for the state border. He knows we can't chase him into another state. Still, we're gaining. We'll catch 'em yet if they don't dodge us in the hills.

A few minutes later —

The cops are catching up on us. This will teach 'em to keep their distance.

Taste this, cops!

And, as the gangster opened fire —

This is where I get off!

Bang goes a tyre. Hurry up and change it!

That's these guys clean away. Captain Logan's gonna have something to say about that. Hey, where's the Limey?

He took off through the door when machine-gun Gurney blasted us. He could've busted his fool neck.

I told you that Big Palooka was yellow. He'd rather risk a broken neck than face bullets. Well, he can stay here. We're going on when the wheel is fixed. He can find his own way home!

Later —

Step on it, Donovan. We're in luck. Some rocks have blocked the road and halted Weist's car.

Me.262
THE FIRST
JET FIGHTER

IN 1944, the Mustang and Thunderbolt fighters escorting American bombers deep into Germany were more than a match for the German piston-engined fighters which had so far opposed them. But a severe set-back to their superiority came blazing into action, in the deadly shape of the Messerschmitt 262, the world's first operational jet fighter!

The Me 262 story began in 1939, when Messerschmitt were asked to design an airframe for an exciting new engine development—the jet!

But the airframe was ready too soon for the engines, so the first Me 262 took the air with a piston engine! Even when the jet engines were fitted, this was retained. It was just as well for the test-pilot, as the experimental engines cut out on his second landing approach!

One disadvantage of the design was the conventional wheel layout that meant the jet tail-pipes pointed downwards. This was very bad for runways!

It also meant a difficult and dangerous take-off technique! The Me 262 had a very high lift-off speed—and to raise the tailplane, the pilot had to apply the brake sharply at 100 m.p.h.! The Luftwaffe test pilot later chosen to demonstrate the plane totally misjudged his speed—and finished his take-off run in a rubbish tip!

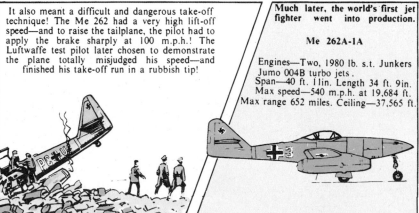

Much later, the world's first jet fighter went into production.

Me 262A-1A

Engines—Two, 1980 lb. s.t. Junkers Jumo 004B turbo jets.
Span—40 ft. 11in. Length 34 ft. 9in.
Max speed—540 m.p.h. at 19,684 ft.
Max range 652 miles. Ceiling—37,565 ft.

The next setback to the Me 262 came when Hitler, the Nazi leader, insisted the jet should be used purely as a bomber! This brought its speed right down to within that of piston-engined Allied fighters!

SAY, WE'RE CATCHING UP ON THESE JET-BIRDS!

LET'S HIT 'EM NOW, BEFORE THEY DROP THEIR BOMBS!

The war dragged on, with the promising Me 262 being produced only slowly and then misused. But with things going badly for Germany, fighter versions soon flew again, to defend their homeland. The jets scored some success as night - fighters, against Mosquitos, over Berlin.

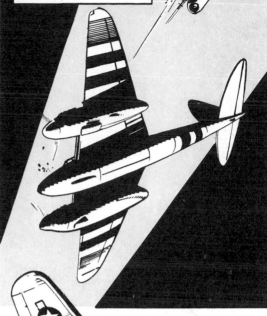

But only 100 or so jet fighters got into operation. In disgust, the General of Fighters, Adolf Galland gave up his high position to form an elite squadron of 262's, staffed by the cream of the Luftwaffe's pilots, not one less than Captain in rank!

The jets struck again and again at the Allied bombers, achieving successes out of all proportion to their small numbers. Galland's squadron scored hits against the American Fortresses, using the latest fighter weapon —rockets!

But sheer numbers of Allied aircraft soon told, and materials for building the jets became more and more scarce. Soon every single Me 262 was so precious they were allowed to take off—their most defenceless moment—only under a protecting umbrella of Fw 190 fighters!

At last, American bombing struck at the bases of the jets. Thrown into the struggle too late and in insufficient numbers, the world's first jet-fighters were destroyed on the ground, when they could have put up a fight for mastery of the air!

Now he owes you for a new bike, huh?

Joe Sculloni, eh? He used to be a top hit man for the Mafia but now takes outside killing contracts. Obviously likes to use small fry for his dirty work. He runs a pool hall at Oak Bluffs!

At Oak Bluffs —

Park your hardware at my office, Bearpaw. I don't want no scalp-huntin' in this town.

POOL HALL

COUNTY SHERIFF'S OFFICE

Just figurin' on a friendly game of pool, Sheriff.

Any of you guys fancy a game for fifty grand?

The lousy Injun tried to knife us, Al!

Yeah, when we caught him cheatin' at pool! So we had to waste him in self defence, Tod!

You missed!

URRGH!

CRASH!

You guys are just 'way out of your league!

Ugh! Can't breathe! My throat!

You'll be breathing blood if I slit it, punk! Where's Joe Sculloni?

Pardon me for bustin' in like this, Sculloni!

No sweat, Jay! You bust up the pool-room, rough up the customers, then get shot trying to rob this office.

PRIVATE

CRASH!

EEARGH!

That puts you behind the eight-ball, Pal! Now I'd best get you off to jail!

You're dead, Jay! I wasn't the only one aiming to pick up that contract on you. Rafe Gomez and Max Keller are in on it, too.

You'll sure need this hardware with top hit-men like Gomez and Keller on your trail, Bearpaw! Wonder who's hired 'em?

Some jerk who figures my scalp's worth fifty grand. He must have sent a few grand up front to all three of these creeps, the rest to come after the contract's completed.

Next day at Snake Fork ranch . .

No trail bike today, Bearpaw?

No, I figure it makes me kinda conspicuous for these hoods who're gunnin' for me, Clint. So I'll just stick around like one of your hired cow-punchers and take a ride over to Coyote Gulch.

Get 'phoning, Clint Calhoun! With old buddies like you who needs enemies?

Gomez? You could hit pay dirt at Coyote Gulch.

Later —

Sure hot out here! No two-legged coyote shown up yet.

THUD!

Gomez still using his cross-bow! Aims to miss first shot to laugh at his target panicking!

Hey, why you not shoot or run, eh? You wanna spoil my fun?

Yeah, we Injuns got no sense of humour, Gomez.

Jay fired his rifle then . . .

Like, we shoot to scare our own ponies . . .

Madre mia! Not good target in water splashing!

61

And we clobber clowns before they can re-load.!

Thanks, pal! Lousy stunt of mine puttin' you to drink just across from where I guessed that joker might bush-whack us.

Back at the ranch . . .

Gomez was riding a horse with your brand, Clint. You fingered me to Sculloni and his biker hoodlums, too.

I — I — they threatened me and my folks, Bearpaw. I'd no choice!

Well, now I need fast wheels — and maybe a gentle hint about where to look for Max Keller.

He — er — rented that old prospector's shack out at Cactus Rocks.

Just cutting off your phone, Clint. I'll call the Highway Patrol from a road-box to come and take Gomez off your hands.

Max Keller — a Kraut who served in the French Foreign Legion when I was out in 'Nam. Nearly sun-down. Bad approach if Keller's on guard.

Yeah, he's sure on sentry duty — with a bazooka!

You are slipping, Jay! Never attack with setting sun in your eyes!

I guessed you might soon deal with Sculloni and Gomez. So I just waited for your visit here.

He's right! Knocking off punks can make a guy careless! But I'll just pump some lead his way.

Then force him to blast these wheels with his bazooka!

BRRRM!

And so blow his own cover!

Sub-machine gun fire now! This joker's a one-man army!

That's better, Jay! You'd best run for the rocks!

Watch out for mines! I scattered a few small ones there!

Lost my rifle! Blast caught my ankle! Boy, am I getting blown away here!

What's this he's stirred up here?

A rattler! Poor critter's scared by all this aggro!

Next moment —

Lieber Gott! A snake! Aargh! I'm bitten.

Tough luck on the rattler! It may die of rat poison!

Help me, Jay! You Indians know about snake bites.

Enough to know you're cold meat, Keller, unless you've got wheels to get to hospital at Oak Bluff mighty fast.

I was a fool to pick up that contract on you! Do you know who put it out?

SCREEECH!

Yeah, a guy called Bearpaw Jay!

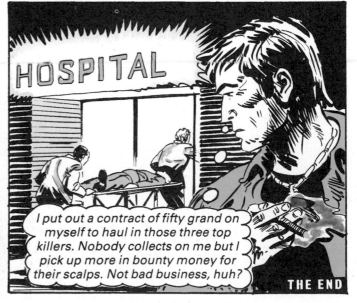

HOSPITAL

I put out a contract of fifty grand on myself to haul in those three top killers. Nobody collects on me but I pick up more in bounty money for their scalps. Not bad business, huh?

THE END

SPRING-HEELED JACK

JOHN JACKSON, the, quiet, mild-mannered civilian clerk at Ravell Row Police Station in Victorian London, had a secret identity... Spring-Heeled Jack, deadly enemy of the underworld. One day, a station errand took him to Brandon Arcade, when suddenly...

AAAAH!

EEAAH!

Stand back! Let me through! I'm a doctor!

I've been robbed!

So have I! Damned looters!

Later, at Ravell Row Police Station—

Another anarchist bomb! Jackson, write what I dictate...

Yes, Sergeant Drew!

I recognise him. He's a sneak thief and pick-pocket!

AAAAAH!

I meant no 'arm. I . . . I snatched it from some toff near the docks. That's the truth!

He's no looter — that's for sure!

Swiftly Jackson returned home—

Hmm! A doctor's bag! I'll soon find out to whom it belongs.

Next morning—

I found it yesterday, Doctor Kirby.

I'm so grateful. It must have fallen from my pony trap.

I treat London's poor for no charge! Luckily I carry a spare . . .

He didn't mention that the bag was snatched near the docks. Very strange! He also helped at the arcade! The good doctor might be worth keeping an eye on.

A week later—

You three will travel with the mail train tonight. It not only carries passengers but high value mail. It's just the target for the bombers and looters.

Particularly if there's a criminal mastermind behind it all! I think Spring-heeled Jack should have a look into this.

I'll check in my own way. The passengers may give a clue.

The devil from the fog! What's he carrying?

Gentlemen — the bombers, with the compliments of Spring-Heeled Jack

'E planned it! 'E carried the bombs!

Shut up, you fool!

Back at the station—

Where on Earth have you been skulking, Jackson? Come down here at once!

C-Coming, S-Sergeant.

My trap caught them! Lucky I had men on the train. I'm having the doctor's surgery searched.

Next morning, Drew reported to his superior—

I always suspected the doctor. His bag was ideal for carrying a bomb. I had my suspicions, sir. We found the bomb-making materials there too!

Good work, Sergeant.

Sir, Spring-heeled Jack brought them to us. He . . .

Silence, Constable! That's enough imaginative nonsense. Jackson, don't dare write down any of that! We deal in facts!

Er . . . very good Sergeant!

The End

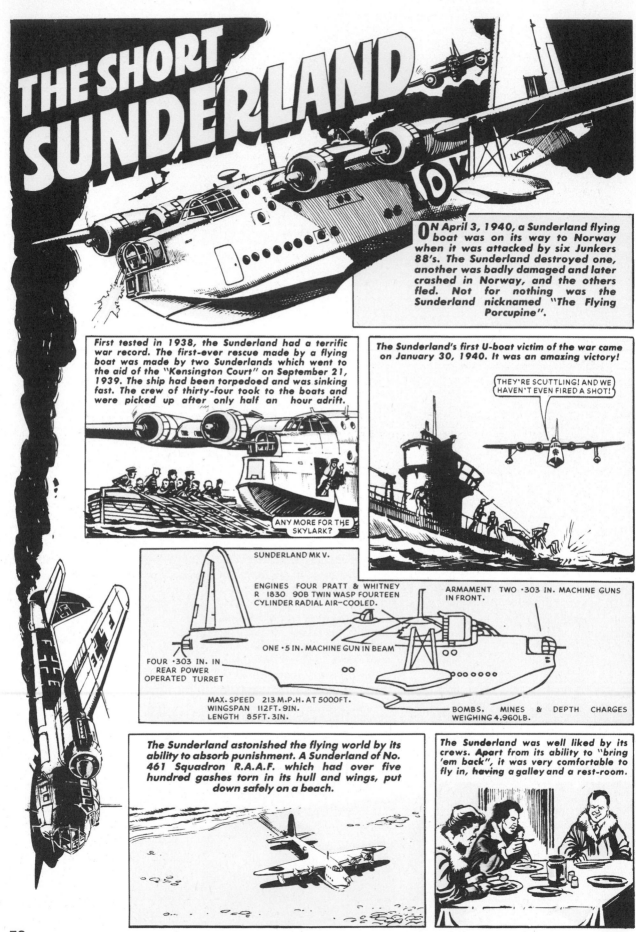

THE SHORT SUNDERLAND

ON April 3, 1940, a Sunderland flying boat was on its way to Norway when it was attacked by six Junkers 88's. The Sunderland destroyed one, another was badly damaged and later crashed in Norway, and the others fled. Not for nothing was the Sunderland nicknamed "The Flying Porcupine".

First tested in 1938, the Sunderland had a terrific war record. The first-ever rescue made by a flying boat was made by two Sunderlands which went to the aid of the "Kensington Court" on September 21, 1939. The ship had been torpedoed and was sinking fast. The crew of thirty-four took to the boats and were picked up after only half an hour adrift.

ANY MORE FOR THE SKYLARK?

The Sunderland's first U-boat victim of the war came on January 30, 1940. It was an amazing victory!

THEY'RE SCUTTLING! AND WE HAVEN'T EVEN FIRED A SHOT!

SUNDERLAND MK V.

ENGINES FOUR PRATT & WHITNEY R 1830 90B TWIN WASP FOURTEEN CYLINDER RADIAL AIR-COOLED.

ARMAMENT TWO ·303 IN. MACHINE GUNS IN FRONT.

ONE ·5 IN. MACHINE GUN IN BEAM.

FOUR ·303 IN. IN REAR POWER OPERATED TURRET

MAX. SPEED 213 M.P.H. AT 5000FT.
WINGSPAN 112FT. 9IN.
LENGTH 85FT. 3IN.

BOMBS, MINES & DEPTH CHARGES WEIGHING 4,960LB.

The Sunderland astonished the flying world by its ability to absorb punishment. A Sunderland of No. 461 Squadron R.A.A.F. which had over five hundred gashes torn in its hull and wings, put down safely on a beach.

The Sunderland was well liked by its crews. Apart from its ability to "bring 'em back", it was very comfortable to fly in, having a galley and a rest-room.

Coastal Command's main job was to protect shipping. The long hours of inactivity, protecting convoys, were often interrupted very abruptly.

THE TANKER'S BEEN TORPEDOED! I'M GOING DOWN TO HAVE A LOOK.

One of the strangest adventures of the war befell a Sunderland crew when their plane crashed in Libyan waters. Floating on a wing, they drifted on to a beach . . .

JUST OUR LUCK. CAPTURED BY ITALIAN TROOPS!

Left in an Arab village, the British prisoners enlisted the help of a local who promised to lead them to the British lines. When the Italians discovered what was going on, they threw down their weapons and gave themselves up! By the time the airmen got to their own lines, they had over a hundred Italian prisoners!

Spotting subs at night was an extremely difficult task, but by the end of the war Sunderlands had accounted for over half the German U-boats destroyed.

Bad weather forced a pilot to land his Sunderland in an Icelandic fiord. The plane landed safely, but—

WE'VE HIT A SHOAL!

Luckily, the plane was undamaged and next morning the tide refloated the plane. The next problem was to fly to another part of Iceland for fuel. Take off was difficult as the fiord was only 50 yards wide and the plane's wingspan was 38! The pilot made his attempt in the afternoon . . .

PHEW! JUST MADE IT!

Unfortunately, the crews' problems weren't yet over. When filling the fuel tank water got in and the whole fuel system, tanks and all, had to be emptied and thoroughly cleaned. This took four days! Again the tanks were filled and the Sunderland took off, only to be forced back by an electrical storm!

The crew flew to Scotland safely next day.

The 748 Sunderlands built earned a tremendous reputation. And their services didn't end with the war. Airlines of New South Wales (Australia) operated a service to the tiny Pacific island of Lord Howe until very recently . . .

THIS IS A DINKUM RUN, EH SPORT? YOU'RE ALWAYS SURE OF A TERRIFIC WELCOME!

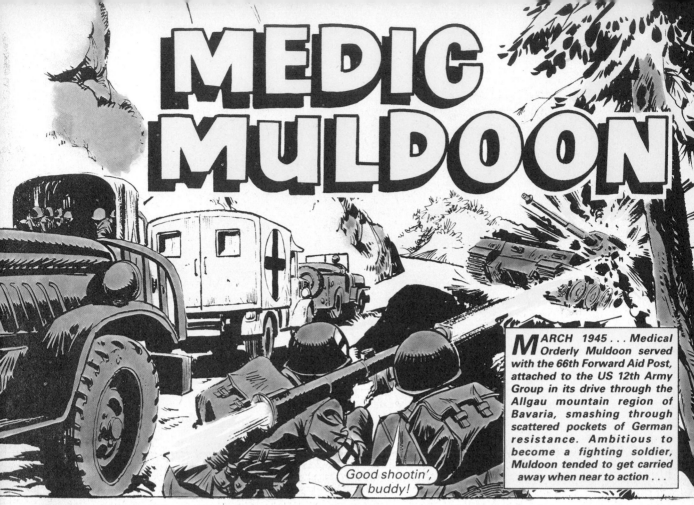

MEDIC MULDOON

MARCH 1945 . . . Medical Orderly Muldoon served with the 66th Forward Aid Post, attached to the US 12th Army Group in its drive through the Allgau mountain region of Bavaria, smashing through scattered pockets of German resistance. Ambitious to become a fighting soldier, Muldoon tended to get carried away when near to action . . .

Good shootin', buddy!

Son, you must be the first medic to wipe out a Tiger tank. Your C.O. is likely to put you in for a medal when he gets my report.

Hum — er, a medal ain't what he'll be handing out, sir.

Major Parkin had his own way of rewarding Muldoon's military efforts—

URRGH!

Don't you EVER listen, Muldoon?

Sending you forward to collect casualties does not mean you causing some of your own. We are NOT killers, but HEALERS!

Yessir! I only wish I was a natural man of peace like you, sir!

I don't believe it. Yes, it IS him!

HOLZ, OLD FRIEND! GUSTAV HOLZ!

Parkin? It is really you, old fellow? Often have I wondered what became of Professor Simpkin's best pupil.

No, Gustav, you were always the best. I expected that by now you would be head of surgery In some Berlin hospital.

No, old chap, I became just a humble army doctor. Now myself and these are your prisoners.

Gustav, I am not wasting your skill. We shall work together.

Muldoon, we have a new member in our theatre team.

If you say so, sir.

Somebody's watching from that roof.

Yeah, there he is . . . somebody with a rifle!

GET DOWN!

A sniper! I got him! Go get him, you guys!

Some poor crazed wretch who cannot accept the war is lost. I apologise, my friend!

Not the first time I've been shot at, old chap. Muldoon does have his uses.

That night Gustav Holz joined Parkin's unit in the busy operating theatre —

Muldoon, I'll finish here while you go and watch my old classmate. You might learn something.

Come the morning—

I would be grateful if you could send a message to my family. They are evacuated to our mountain chalet not far from here!

After the way you worked tonight, I'll run you there myself!

Half an hour later, after obtaining clearance—

Inform Captain Ripley that he is in charge until my return — and, Muldoon, do try to keep out of trouble.

Yessir!

Later still—

We picked up that sniper, Muldoon! Seems like he's some type of displaced person — and he sure tells a wild story.

Huh!

That's a concentration camp number, Mac!

Ach so, but a special camp — Unit-Nine . . . a place where people like me were experimented on with foul poisons and gasses . . .

. . . Evil conducted by the man you saved from my bullet.

I alone escaped when Unit-Nine was closed and the survivors machine-gunned. I followed Herr Doktor Holz when he fled in the disguise of a Wehrmacht medical officer. I stole a rifle and —

That's enough, buddy. I'm persuaded! Sarge, I need wheels and a weapon. Lucky I know where they've gone!

Meanwhile, Parkin and Holz were well on their way—

This is Bandit country according to army intelligence, Gustav.

Relax, my friend! There have been no military operations in this area.

My chalet. No doubt the noise of our engine has frightened my family into hiding.

Holy Toledo! Those are Death's-Head SS, Gustav!

My brothers in arms, old chap — a kind of family. Behave yourself, Parkin — or I shall be sadly compelled to kill you!

Such a relief, Gustav. We began to think the Americans had you in the bag.

They almost did. I had to adopt the guise of a dutiful Wehrmacht medical officer running a hospital.

You goldarned Nazi.

URRGH!

American dog!

GNNGH!

I'll kill him.

Not now, Gustav. Later we drop him off a crag, but now we get the jewellery.

Gentlemen, our key to a new life — plunder from the wretches disposed of at Unit-Nine.

Let's get it to the truck!

Just then—

Listen! An engine.

A motor-cyclist.

Just one man. Dispose of him while I get our property to the truck!

That must be the place — and there's the major's jeep. It's all so peaceful and inviting.

Reckon I'll send the bike on ahead.

ROOO

Here he comes, Karl — to his death.

HIMMEL! The machine is riderless!

I'm over here, guys!

AAGH!

URRGH!

SERGEANT SIXTY

Surrender or be destroyed!

AD 2600, and the Space-freighter "Vega", carrying valuable corium crystals, was in Sector 24 when the Moonmen struck. No Galactic raiders had ever been better equipped, or more advanced in technology . . .

They've knocked out our engines — we've no choice. Contact Space police control before they come aboard.

Sergeant Sixty was in charge of the Galactic Police in Sector 24—

Scramble! Head for reference 451 326 with all possible speed.

Sixty to force. We'll hit the raiders once they're clear of the freighter. We don't want to cause any civilian casualties!

F

The freighter was being looted—

Move it! Space cops en route!

They've moved away from the freighter! Open fire! Second laser power.

You've got it.

Our laser's been blocked. There must be a force field round their ship.

The moonship fired back—

AAAAAH!

If you space cops want burying, you're in business. Your lasers can't touch us! Now get out of our way!

Our lasers are meant to penetrate ANY force field! We'd best get back to base and report this!

At Sector 24 H.Q.—

Well, Captain? Any idea why our lasers didn't penetrate?

YOU'RE the one in charge of operations in Sector 24, Sixty — YOU find the answers!

Two days later, on an asteroid in the Sector—

Look out! A bank raid! It's those Moonmen we've been hearing about!

Guards gave chase, but—

Their suits are deflecting the rays! Radio police H.Q!

Nothing can stand up to us! Make for the Moonship! Another mission successfully accomplished!

EEAAGH!

We failed! They can simply plunder at will. No one can stop them!

When the report reached Sergeant Sixty—

Why the museum, Sarge?

Because this is where we're going to learn just how to deal with the Moonmen!

In the archives, three pictures held Sixty's attention—

HMM! I wonder . . .!

Can you make the items shown in these diagrams?

I see you've listed old materials now almost forgotten. We can manage, though.

At the briefing room—

This is where we think they'll strike next. We've made it particularly tempting.

So, at wealth-complex Zeta, Sixty arranged unusual defences—

It's a catapult like the Romans once used.

Seems crazy to me! He wants to use a weapon thousands of years old!

NOW!

What — ?

A net! It'll foul our engines! We'll have to clear it before we can take off!

It's time for the bolas! Let 'em have it!

AAARRRGHH!

GOTCHA!

They're panicking! We'll soon deal with them now!

AAARGH!

AAAAGHHH!

WHOOOOSHH!!

No you don't! No one gets away!

Sergeant Sixty's old-fashioned weapons soon had the Moonmen completely demoralised—

We're trapped! We can't get out for this net!

We have your comrades! Surrender! You can't escape!

What devilish weapons are those?

Crossbows! Don't tempt us to try them!

Sixty quickly returned to HQ where he carried out a test—

A Moonman suit doesn't deflect a bolt. I did wonder!

ZAP!

But how do these work when our more modern weapons fail!

The Moonmen have developed an armour that used the heat from our shots to strengthen it when it was hit. The weapons that defeated them used no heat at all so penetrated the armour!

THE END

THE ME 163 KOMET

ONE of the most advanced fighters to come out of the Second World War was Messerschmitt's tubby little rocket fighter. It appeared in the skies over Germany too late to have much effect, but it gave Allied bomber crews quite a fright!

Incredibly, the deadly little machine was developed from an experimental glider! Test pilots found that without the motor, the airframe was a joy to fly.

The rocket motor had originally been designed for installing on aircraft wings to carry out roll tests.

The experimental fighter made its first powered flight in August, 1941. In October of that year, Dittmar, the test-pilot, reached a speed of 623 m.p.h. within 2 minutes of firing his rocket! But the aircraft then lost stability and went into an uncontrollable dive which Dittmar only mastered by cutting the engine.

With more development, it was used for assisted take-offs, then boosted still more for the interceptor.

The Me 163 landed not on wheels but on a retractable skid. Contact with the runway on landing sometimes caused sparks, igniting any rocket fuel left in the tanks—

Trials with an improved motor and modified airframe at Peenemunde were interrupted by American bombing and more delay was caused.

More Me 163's were lost in this way than in actual combat!

At last, in May 1944, the defence squadrons were ready to receive the operational version of the "Komet", as the rocket fighter had come to be known.

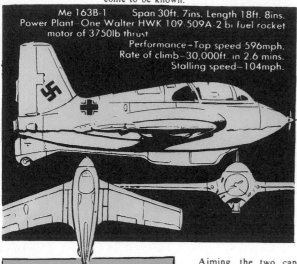

Me 163B-1 Span 30ft. 7ins. Length 18ft. 8ins.
Power Plant—One Walter HWK 109-509A-2 bi-fuel rocket motor of 3750lb thrust
Performance—Top speed 596mph.
Rate of climb—30,000ft. in 2.6 mins.
Stalling speed—104mph.

Delivering the first armed Me 163—B1 to a squadron for weapons testing, chief test-pilot Rudolph Opitz was surprised to find himself the target of the airfield defence guns!

RUDOLPH OPITZ

Fortunately, the Komet arrived in a near-vertical dive, then reduced speed from 500 m.p.h. to 150 m.p.h. all so quickly that the gunners were unable to adjust their sights quick enough.

For his highly dangerous pioneer flying on the rocket fighter, Kapitan Opitz was later awarded the German Cross.

Aiming the two cannon at rocket speed was difficult.

One attempt to overcome the problem was made with upward-firing rockets. A B-17 bomber wing was attached to balloons and when the attacking fighters passed under the target, its shadow caused a photo-electric cell to fire the rockets.

LOOK, THE ROCKETS HAVE RUN OUTA STEAM!

The first squadrons of Komets were sent to protect vital synthetic fuel factories. But so short was their powered duration that the American bombers simply approached from a different angle, and by the time the Komets reached them, they were running out of fuel.

The Germans tried all sorts of tricks to make the short-range fighter effective. They had it towed within range of the bombers. They dived on the bombers from above, they barrel-rolled up through the formations. Kapitan Olejnik perfected the system of roller-coasting attacks through the formation, then turning to reverse the procedure.

But the bombers found the factories that made the rocket fuel before the Me 163 could be made in sufficient numbers to drive them off. The rocket fighters were forced to evacuate their airfields, wallowing helplessly behind towplanes. Their country was soon defeated, and the short but brilliant day of the Komet was over.

THE THING FROM THE PIT

Watch out! We've broken through into something!

The engineers didn't say anything about caves or anything here, Don!

DON REES and Bob Morgan were operating a drill during the morning shift at the Welsh Ellendale Colliery, when . . .

A chamber! But there's nothing here!

Look! There's something on that wall.

"Beware of the Light Shadow!" What does that mean? Whoever heard of a Light Shadow?

BEWARE OF THE LIGHT SHADOW

I'll bet it's that crowd on the night shift! They cooked this up to have us on!

Come on! Let's get back to work. The others will be here soon!

Hang on a minute . . .

Don continued to drill—

It's collapsing . . . breaking through!

For crying out loud— it's another cavern.

Look, what's that?

Here! What's going on, you two?

It's like a giant man . . . shining!

The Light Shadow? Surely not?

It . . . it's moving!

Quick, get back!

It's after us! Blimey! It's exploded the drill!

Make for the lift. It could be our only chance!

That's everyone! Let's get up to the surface.

At the surface—

We're safe! It couldn't get in the lift.

Suddenly—

There it is! It must have come up on the conveyor belt.

We were warned! That inscription in the rock was right.

I'll ram the thing! Hang on!

No! No! Don't go near it!

It's dissolving into a cloud of black powder!

It . . . it's reforming!

No! NO!

EEAAGH!

Don, it's taking over the cab!

Run for you lives! It's driving straight at us!

WOW! That was close!

It's got to be stopped! I'm going after it!

I'm with Don! You others, warn someone. Give the alarm.

Okay, Bob!

It's coming after us! It means revenge!

We'd better go! Those flames will have made it stronger than ever!

The engine won't restart! Run for it!

We're done for! We'll never escape!

Save your breath and keep going! It's gaining on us!

I know where we are. There's a disused mine-working ahead — the Galleybrook ruin. Make for there!

We'll never hide from it.

I've an idea! If my theory about light is right there's just one chance!

Make for the old main shaft!

Why? We'll be trapped!

The entrance was padlocked—

KRAAAANG!!

Hurry, Don! Hurry!

You fool! The floor's gone. We'll fall through!

Keep close to the wall. It's safe enough there!

This is it! If my idea is wrong— we're dead men!

The creature lurched forward—

Good! It's so intent on us, it hasn't noticed the hole!

It's worked! The floor's given way!

Okay, Bob. You can stop panicking now!

The Thing came from the depths— it's gone back!

They've found us! Our lads must've guessed where we were headed!

Fill the shaft in! Bury whatever the Thing was.

It's all hard to believe. But we'll do it. The shaft should have been sealed long before. We'll have lorries of rubble here in minutes.

The Manager was as good as his word—

The Thing's gone back where it belonged. I've a hunch we're all safe now.

This is one report I'm not quite sure how to make out. No one will believe it. Where did that thing come from?

We don't know and I don't suppose we ever will! Just be thankful we won this time!

THE END

96

Better miss these rocks and hit the deep pool or you're a gonner, Rocky me boy!

FILM stuntman, Rocky Rhodes, was filming on location at Carl Driscoll's circus. The film was being made in a rush to have it screened before "The Big Top", a rival production being made by Boss Cantrell. Now Rocky performed one of the most daring stunts . . .

ROCKY RHODES

KING OF THE STUNT MEN

Me and the bike better part company. Don't want it falling on me!

THAT!!

But Rocky's opponent was, by no means, out...

Now, let's see your face—Agh!

Seconds later—

What's going on round here? I was on my way to find what all the excitement was about and some guy almost knocked me over—then I found Rocky out cold!

At least we got to the fire in time, thanks to you guys. And none of the animals was injured.

But you've still got a traitor in the camp—and we've got to find him!

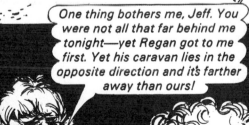

Later—

One thing bothers me, Jeff. You were not all that far behind me tonight—yet Regan got to me first. Yet his caravan lies in the opposite direction and it's farther away than ours!

So, what are you getting at?

So what was he doing out at that time of night? And if he was the guy who clobbered me—all he had to do was ditch that clown mask and the sweater and 'find' me just as you and Carl turned up!

That figures! And who had a better opportunity to goad Satan just before he let him into the cage!

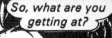

102

Have it your own way. I'm letting Satan off the lead!

No, don't! I'll talk! It was Boss Cantrell paid me to sabotage your circus. He wants to make sure he gets his film out first.

Cantrell! So he's behind all this!

Well, I guess that settles it. I'll call the police.

He's scared his film won't be a big box office success if ours is released first!

It's not quite settled, Carl. We've got to nail Cantrell. I'll make a couple of 'phone calls then I'll tell you what we'll do.

That afternoon, Boss Cantrell received a telephone call . . .

Regan here, Boss. If you switch on your TV set in a few minutes, you'll see what happened at Driscoll's circus last night. I'll see you tonight at the usual place.

Cantrell switched on his TV set and gloated at what he saw!

A mysterious fire broke out at the world-famous Driscoll Wild Animal Circus last night . . .

The fire spread so rapidly that arson is suspected! Hold on, folks! Here's Carl Driscoll, the circus owner!

This is the worst night of my life! A whole life's work has gone up in flames! I am ruined!

That's all I wanted to hear!

That night, in a deserted shack . . .

Well, I've done the job, Boss—now I'll take my pay.

You did a great job, Regan. From the shots I saw on TV, Driscoll's finished—

—and so are you, Regan. You know too much to live. Grab him, boys!

Not this time, buddy!

I'm getting out of here!

OUCH!

You're not going anywhere, Cantrell. Regan told us everything—and, for good measure, we heard everything you said through the microphone Rocky was carrying.

What!

Yes, it was all a set up, Cantrell. And you might like to know that the circus fire was a set up, too.

B-but—those pictures on TV—

You've just seen an exclusive preview of some of the best scenes from our film. Hot stuff, eh!

Oh, no! Me, Boss Cantrell, taken for a sucker!

Later, at the film premiere . . .

Good, they kept the cameras going when you were in the cage, Rocky! And we wrote it into the script!

Afterwards . . .

Great stuff, Rocky! We've a winner on our hands! The press boys loved it! They thought your rescue act was a great bit of acting—and that biker stunt was a real stunner!

If they only knew—

The End

105

B-17 - THE FLYING FORTRESS

IN 1943, an American Boeing B-17 bomber, piloted by Lieutenant Hunter, was crippled by anti-aircraft fire. Falling out of formation, it was set upon by a swarm of Me 109 fighters, over Sicily.

I GOT ONE! THESE NEW SPERRY SIGHTS SURE GET YOU BANG ON THE TARGET.

Hunter's aircraft shot down two of the attackers out of a pack of fifteen—and an hour later, over the Tunisian coast, the gunners got five more! Then with one engine out of action and many controls shot away, the giant bomber made a safe landing!

What kind of bomber could shoot down so many fighters? Begun as a private venture by Boeings, in 1934, the B-17 was the first ever all-metal monoplane bomber, and was faster than any American fighter of that time. Even the earliest models, had an unusual number of machine-guns for defence.

GEE. WOULDYA LOOK AT ALL THOSE GUNS?

IT'S LIKE A FORTRESS— A FLYING FORTRESS!

Very soon, an early B-17 established a new class record by flying from Seattle to New York in 9 hours, 14 minutes— at an average speed of 265 m.p.h.

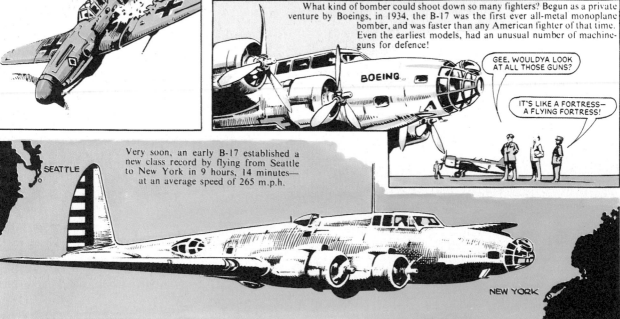

SEATTLE

NEW YORK

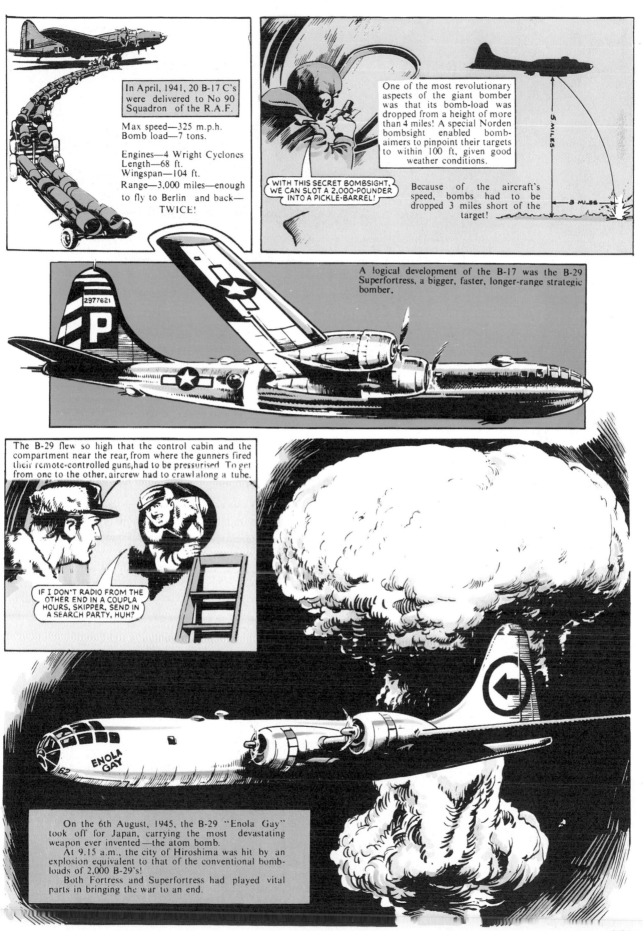

In April, 1941, 20 B-17 C's were delivered to No 90 Squadron of the R.A.F.

Max speed—325 m.p.h.
Bomb load—7 tons.

Engines—4 Wright Cyclones
Length—68 ft.
Wingspan—104 ft.
Range—3,000 miles—enough to fly to Berlin and back— TWICE!

One of the most revolutionary aspects of the giant bomber was that its bomb-load was dropped from a height of more than 4 miles! A special Norden bombsight enabled bomb-aimers to pinpoint their targets to within 100 ft, given good weather conditions.

WITH THIS SECRET BOMBSIGHT, WE CAN SLOT A 2,000-POUNDER INTO A PICKLE-BARREL!

Because of the aircraft's speed, bombs had to be dropped 3 miles short of the target!

5 MILES

3 MILES

A logical development of the B-17 was the B-29 Superfortress, a bigger, faster, longer-range strategic bomber.

The B-29 flew so high that the control cabin and the compartment near the rear, from where the gunners fired their remote-controlled guns, had to be pressurised. To get from one to the other, aircrew had to crawl along a tube.

IF I DON'T RADIO FROM THE OTHER END IN A COUPLA HOURS, SKIPPER, SEND IN A SEARCH PARTY, HUH?

On the 6th August, 1945, the B-29 "Enola Gay" took off for Japan, carrying the most devastating weapon ever invented—the atom bomb.
At 9.15 a.m., the city of Hiroshima was hit by an explosion equivalent to that of the conventional bomb-loads of 2,000 B-29's!
Both Fortress and Superfortress had played vital parts in bringing the war to an end.

LARRY HAD A LOT TO LEARN!

IT was a big day for seventeen-year-old Larry Ricks when Newchester United's talent scout came to watch the St Luke's youth team in action. In twenty-five league matches, St Luke's had conceded only six goals, largely due to Larry's brilliant goalkeeping. Larry's signing for United seemed a certainty . . .

Isn't Larry the greatest? If United don't sign him, then they don't know talent when they see it.

Hmm. There's no doubt Larry Ricks has a great deal of natural ability.

Larry finished the game in fine style, enabling St Luke's to hang on to their 1-0 lead.

How did I do, lads? Do you think Mr Greeson was impressed?

You bet he was, Larry. Look, he's coming over now.

But Larry was disappointed—

He's talking to that striker of St John's, Larry. He didn't even notice you.

I-I guess the United don't need any more goalies.

I was sure Mr Greeson would at least invite me to the United ground for a trial.

Feeling sorry for yourself won't help, Larry. You have the makings of a good goalie, but you have a lot to learn.

I've been doing pretty well in goal for St Luke's for the past two seasons! Anyway, what do you know about goalkeeping, Mister?

Enough to spot a score of mistakes you made today, all of which could have ended in goals, Larry. I think I can help you. Keeper's my name.

What's this? The Goalie Clinic? Huh, a fat lot this Keeper can tell me about goalkeeping.

The following evening—

There's nothing here but open moor. Huh, I should have known that chap was a crank . . .

I'm glad you came, Larry. If you'll follow me we can begin your training right away.

He has great potential, but he is raw. I hope I see him again.

108

Larry learned the hard way—

With practice, Larry began to improve—

Next day—

A week later—

The Keeper had much more to teach him—

A goalie must always be prepared for the unexpected, Larry. A weak shot, or a back pass from a team mate may seem harmless . . .

. . . but watch out for the unexpected bounce.

OOPS!

Concentration is vital, Larry. Let nothing distract you from your job.

Fireworks!

You can often tempt a forward to shoot the way you want him to shoot, Larry. By appearing to expect a shot to your right . . .

. . . you invite him to shoot to your left and have the ball well covered.

Very crafty! I must try that one.

And finally, Larry. We have every goalie's nightmare. The penalty kick. No taker worth his salt should give a goalie a chance to save a penalty.

Here's a tip, though. Watch the taker's standing foot as he takes the kick. It will always always point in the direction he intends to shoot the ball. Then dive that way.

It will give you only a split second's advantage, but with a penalty any advantage is better than none.

I did it! Well — nearly!

I don't know how to thank you! I thought I knew all there was to know about goal-keeping till I came here.

Larry's play improved tremendously over the next few months — and this did not go unobserved—

I've been watching you for a while, Larry. How would you like to play for United?

Just try to remember what you've learned, Larry, and practise, practise, practise!

I-I'd love to Mr O......!

Larry is now United's first team goalie, with a record second to none — but he reckons he's still learning compared with the Keeper!

111

THE END

LORDS OF THE PLAINS – THE STORY OF THE BUFFALO

PART TWO

IN the middle of the Nineteenth Century, when the railways began to spread over America, the buffalo of the plains began to be shot for food.

Then buffalo-hide garments and accessories became highly fashionable in the East and the death knell of the buffalo was sounded.

BUFFALO HIDE DURABLE AND FASHIONABLE

The killing increased, till, in the three years from 1872-74, over 4 million buffalo were slaughtered! Many famous crackshots and peace officers began their careers as buffalo hunters—men like "Buffalo Bill" Cody, who once shot 4,280 animals in eighteen months, Wyatt Earp and Bat Masterton.

Thousands of buffalo were shot by professional hunters accompanied by teams of skinners. Depots were set up to process the hides and send them back East. One such place grew to become Dodge City, the centre of the buffalo industry.

BUFFALO CITY NOW DODGE CITY

"BUFFALO BILL" CODY.   WYATT EARP   BAT MASTERTON.

On the third day of the siege of Adobe Walls, a buffalo hunter took aim at an Indian over 1500 yards away. What seemed like minutes later, the Indian fell dead. The tremendous penetrating power of the Sharps "Big 50" buffalo gun so frightened the Indians that they gave up the fight.

Soon the hunters were moving into Indian lands to get at the buffalo there. Ignoring all treaties, they set up depots like Adobe Walls in Texas. Angered at this, a horde of Indians under Comanche chief Quanah Parker besieged the place.

THE SHARPS 'BIG FIFTY' BUFFALO RIFLE

By the year 1889, about 600 buffalo survived out of millions! The skin trade died out as suddenly as it had begun.

A few far-seeing men collected the last of the buffalo, which were later established in reserves in Canada and America. Today, the Lord of the Plains is carefully protected in national parks— but never again will the prairies of the West thunder to the hoofs of millions.

With less and less buffalo to be found, the Indians grew hungry and desperate. This, more than the efforts of the U.S. Cavalry, subdued them and made the white men masters of the plains.

THE END

THE COONSKIN GRENADIER

He's back! Oh, no — no! You said he'd been lost in Italy, Sergeant-Major Minchin!

Sir John, I got him lost — I swear it! How was I to know he'd steal a train and bring back a Jerry general?

IN 1942, hill-billy Zebadiah Flood was in Britain with the Royal Warrant that made him an Honorary Colonel in the Royal Grenadiers. Colonel Sir John Grogan found him lots to do in far away places but Zeb kept turning up at Potomac Barracks in London — along with Alexander, the ape, and Lightning, the hound . . . and sometimes with the odd surprise . . .

Beg pardon, sir — how if you was to order him on leave? He never disobeys an order.

Leave? In America! Ships get torpedoed — aircraft crash! Now I wonder if that fellow in the USAAF would do me a favour . . .?

A bargain was struck and Zeb was ordered on leave —

That night the Potomac Mess entertained an overseas guest —

A Presidential citation and a priority travel warrant! That is asking a lot, Sir John.

I can offer a lot, old fellow! How about half a dozen cases of that fine old port you so enjoy?

He even insisted on Alexander and the hound coming along with me. That Sir John is all heart, Sarn't-Major.

Orders is orders, Sarn't-Major. I jest hope Sir John can run the war for a whole month without me.

A great man, Honorary Colonel. He almost broke down weeping as he saw us off.

For once I'm glad to go along with him. There's no war and no rationing in America.

118

UNDERWATER WONDERS

One morning, at ex-Royal Navy Brad Jones and Greg Roberts' salvage base —

I'm Brad Jones and this is my partner Greg Roberts. What can we do for you, Mister Trenby?

I've discovered an oyster bed which I'm sure contains a high percentage of black pearls.

The local native divers aren't interested. Something to do with the high number of sharks in the area.

Okay, then! We'll give it a whirl.

Three days later —

There's the island, lads!

Hmm! There can't be many people living on it.

IN July 1944, during World War II, a Japanese Zero shot down a supply-carrying Douglas Dakota over a small Pacific island. A small incident in the war, but it was to have imporant results over forty years later.

That's funny! The natives are being watched by armed guards!

Yeah — what's going on?

Sorry about the deception. Do as you're told and you'll stay in one piece.

He means it! We're up to our necks in trouble here!

There's the wreck of a Nip vessel sunk during the war, just over two hundred feet down! It carried gold — and you're going to get it for me!

That night they were prisoners in a guarded hut —

Even if we do it, Brad, they daren't let us leave here alive.

Next day —

We're over the wreck! Down you go and start bringing that gold up. Don't think of escape — or you'll feed the sharks.

There's the wreck Trenby talked about over there.

And here's the gold — tons of the stuff!

Half an hour later —

That's the first lot. Now get your tanks refilled and keep at it.

Sharks! And we've no weapons — of course! We'll have to move away from the wreck.

An old aircraft! It'll give us some cover!

Phew, too close for comfort.

It must have been shot down in World War II. I wonder what's in these boxes! They're well sealed.

I recognise these boxes from my Navy days! One contains limpet mines — the other, rifles!

W.D.

It's time they surfaced.

Reckon they've had trouble with sharks.

Here's your gold! But it's going to take a long time if those sharks keep driving us off!

That night —

Each time we dive we'll get those cases closer to the island. Our only hope is that the guns and explosives still work.

Another couple of days is probably as much as we can stretch it!

Next day —

Where's Jones?

He's still down, clearing away some debris!

That's far enough for now. I'd better get back and help Greg before Trenby rumbles us!

What the devil happened to you? I'm not stupid! Don't try dragging out this job too long.

If you think you can do better — YOU go down, mate!

Later that day, back on the island —

You are working well, my friends. You should be finished tomorrow!

Tomorrow is now or never for us. We'll get killed no matter what happens!

One of the boxes contained limpet mines! I've left a couple near the wreck. The other box with the guns is in the shallows near the beach.

Next morning —

As soon as we have all the gold, kill them in the water. The sharks will take care of the bodies.

Sure thing, boss!

We'll strike now! They won't be expecting anything just yet.

Let's hope the timing fuses still work.

We'd better get out of here — FAST!

123

They're a long time. Can you see any bubbles?

...sending shock waves to the surface!

What on...?

AAGH!

The limpet mines exploded...

The fools have blown themselves up.

Get back to the island!

These guns were normally pretty well packed! I hope the waterproofing has held out!

Guns AND ammo! Now we'll sort out Trenby and his thugs.

Not if these guns are too badly corroded. Our one hope is to take 'em by surprise.

What happened? The explosion . . .

AAH!

It's them! Spread out, we'll soon take care of them!

Those divers must have exploded something. They'll have been blown to bits.

The natives seized their chance —

OKAY! We give up!

Be smart. Don't give us any trouble! With the natives' help we outnumber you!

Just as well you didn't know our guns siezed up after only one shot. All that time in the salt water was too muoh for them!

Why you . . .!

The American authorities will be glad to see you — and they'll like the gold, too. Should be a nice reward for us — and the natives!

THE END

1933

REX

The "Rex" of the Italia Line took 4 days 13 hours 58 minutes from Gibraltar to Ambrose at an average speed of 28.92 knots.

The BLUE

THE BLUE RIBAND IS THE PRIZE FOR THE SHIP THAT CARRIES OUT THE FASTEST CROSSING OF THE NORTH ATLANTIC. HERE ARE SOME OF THE SHIPS WHO HAVE HELD THAT RECORD.

1986

ATLANTIC CHALLENGER

Atlantic Challenger, Mr Richard Branson's power boat, took 3 days 8 hours and 31 minutes from Ambrose to Bishop Rock at an average speed of 36.5 knots.